Diversification booklet number 13

Farm ponds for water, fish and livelihoods

James W. Miller

Rural Infrastructure and Agro-Industries Division
Food and Agriculture Organization of the United Nations
Rome 2009

The designations employed and the presentation of material in this information product do not imply the expression of any opinion whatsoever on the part of the Food and Agriculture Organization of the United Nations (FAO) concerning the legal or development status of any country, territory, city or area or of its authorities, or concerning the delimitation of its frontiers or boundaries. The mention of specific companies or products of manufacturers, whether or not these have been patented, does not imply that these have been endorsed or recommended by FAO in preference to others of a similar nature that are not mentioned.

The views expressed in this information product are those of the authors and do not necessarily reflect the views of FAO.

ISBN 978-92-5-106141-1

Table of contents

Preface

The purpose of the FAO Diversification booklets is to raise awareness and provide decision support information about opportunities at farm and local community level to increase the incomes of small-scale farmers.

Each booklet focuses on a farm or non-farm enterprise that can be integrated into small farms to increase incomes and enhance livelihoods. The enterprises profiled in the FAO Diversification booklets are suitable for smallholder farmers in terms of resource requirements, additional costs, exposure to risk and complexity. The products or services generated by the enterprises are suitable for meeting demand on a growing, or already strong, local market and are not dependent on an export market.

The main target audience for these booklets are people and organizations that provide advisory, business and technical support services to resource-poor small-scale farmers and local communities in low- and middle-income countries. It is hoped that enough information is given to help these support service providers to consider new income-generating opportunities and how these might enable small-scale farmers to take action. What are the potential benefits? What are farmer requirements and constraints? What are critical 'success factors'?

The FAO Diversification booklets are also targeted to policy-makers and programme managers in government and non-governmental organizations. What actions might policy-makers take to create enabling environments for small-scale farmers to diversify into new income-generating activities?

The FAO Diversification booklets are not intended to be technical 'how to do it' guidelines. Readers will need to seek more information or technical support, so as to provide farmer advisory and support activities relating to the introduction of new income-generating activities. To assist in this respect, each booklet identifies additional sources of information, technical support and website addresses.

A CD has been prepared with a full series of FAO Diversification booklets and FAO technical guides, together with complementary guides on market research, financing, business planning, etc. Copies of the CD are available on request from FAO. FAO Diversification booklets can also be downloaded from the FAO Internet site.

If you find this booklet of value, we would like to hear from you. Tell your colleagues and friends about it. FAO would welcome suggestions about possible changes for enhancing our next edition or regarding relevant topics for other booklets. By sharing your views and ideas with us we can provide better services to you.

Acknowledgements

Gratitude is owed to Matthias Halwart, Fisheries Resource Officer, Aquaculture Management and Conservation Service (FIMA), FAO. His precious time, support and endurance, enabled this booklet to be within the FAO Diversification series. He successfully managed the entire production process for this booklet, coordinating with the author and internal reviewers in FIMA, as well as Drs Mark Prein and Rohana Subasinghe, and also liaising with the Rural Infrastructure and Agro-Industries (AGS) Division of FAO. Special thanks are also owed to Dr. John Moehl, Aquaculture Officer, Regional Office for Africa, FAO, for his support and contributions to the writing of this booklet. Further, a particular mention and a big thank you is owed to Pedro Bueno, formerly Director General of the Network of Aquaculture Centres in Asia-Pacific, for his reviews, contributions and writing.

Acknowledgements for the series
Gratitude is owed to Doyle Baker, Chief, Rural Infrastructure and Agro-Industries Division (AGS), FAO, for his vision, encouragement and constant support in the development of the FAO Diversification booklet series. Thanks are also due to Josef Kienzle, Agro-Industries Officer, AGS, FAO, for his patience, commitment, and contributions to the production and post-production of the series. Clare Bishop-Sambrook, principal editor of the series, provided technical support and guidance, both during the development and finalization of the booklets. Martin Hilmi provided both technical and editorial inputs and managed the post-production phase of the series. Fabio Ricci undertook the design and layout of the booklets and desktop publishing.

Farm ponds for water, fish and livelihoods

Servicing smallholders

Smallholder farmers make up 70 percent of the population of many developing countries. With limited resources, they manage multiple activities in crop and animal production to spread risk and sustain their households. However, they are overlooked in public assistance programmes and services, which are often biased towards the bigger and better organized farmers. Numerous smallholders have less influence on policy, poor access to support services and technical inputs. They are generally seen to have a lower contribution to national food supply, and the cost of servicing them is considered as disproportionately high.

Small rural producers, particularly in remote areas, face difficulties in physical access to markets, placing constraints on the volumes and types of products they can produce, and restricting their potential to benefit from the growing demand in farm products. These problems are made worse by the lack of post-harvest facilities for highly perishable products, such as fish, and weak links to markets.

Farm ponds can provide for a number of benefits that can help smallholders in their quest for development. They provide for water storage, can be used to rear fish and other aquatic organisms like crustaceans, molluscs and plants, be integrated with other farm enterprises and improve and vary farm family diets. Further and importantly farm ponds can contribute to income and employment.

▪ *Lessons from the past*
Early efforts to promote farm ponds were aimed at having large numbers of small ponds. Numerous small ponds were built with little attention to quality and availability of fish seed, nutrient inputs, extension support, capital, and market. National programmes seemed to have been influenced more by a political agenda rather than a purely rural development agenda. This resulted in too many ponds being dug, many of which were poorly sited and constructed, with insufficient technical support.

Members of these early programmes were mostly subsistence farmers with limited land and few

Farm ponds for water, fish and livelihoods

other resources. Some of the farmers in these programmes saw opportunities to earn profits and their farming models became the forerunner of more recent systems that combined the objectives of producing fish for home consumption as well as for the market. The few viable farms that survived now serve as a positive lesson in sustainable smallholder farming systems. However, the majority that failed, caused by pitfalls in programmes, lack of planning, and badly targeted technical support have also provided instructive lessons on rural development strategies: they in particular taught the lesson that projects need to be sustainable and not foster direct dependence.

■ *Understanding the situation and context of smallholders*

Aquaculture has been recognized as an important component of rural development strategies aimed at improving food supply and generating more income for poor farming households. To understand their circumstances better, the categorization 'commercial' and 'non-commercial' has been devised. To clearly define the target group for support programmes, it is necessary to understand non-commercial and commercial fish farming. Experience over the past decades has shown that

FIGURE 1   Fish ponds in the People's Republic of China
(Photo: © FAO/20044/H. Zhang)

few farmers make the transformation from non-commercial to commercial farming. Those who do, expand or intensify their operations and their experiences, and the drivers that made them undertake the transition need to be examined and promoted. Figure 2 illustrates the value chains of each category.

Smallholder farmers have a poorly developed non-commercial, non-market oriented value chain. In contrast, commercial fish farmers require and usually have extensive and generally reliable support from upstream input suppliers and downstream handlers, processors and marketers.

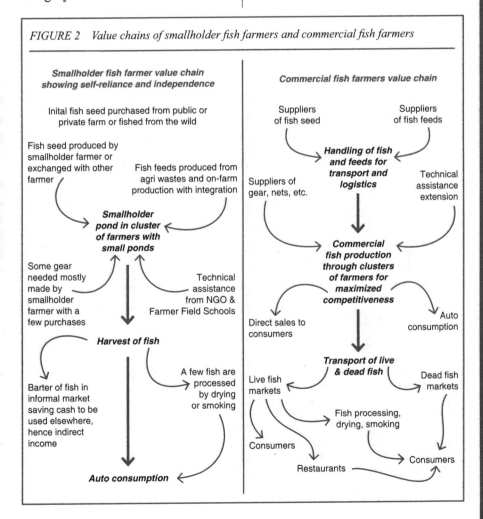

FIGURE 2 Value chains of smallholder fish farmers and commercial fish farmers

Farm ponds for water, fish and livelihoods

Returns from improved services

Appropriately targeted assistance to smallholder farmers can provide high returns. Planned and implemented interventions can facilitate assistance that, above all outcomes, makes farmers self-reliant rather than dependent on the public sector, NGOs and donors. The ultimate pay-off can be: organized and better informed farmers; progressive farms that are not abandoned when grants or external assistance terminate; higher and sustained productivity; marketable surpluses; and higher family earnings. Desirable effects of these gains would be the private sector seeking profitable business opportunities with smallholders and the public sector providing better services and capital goods such as roads and energy supply. Smallholders, then, could contribute more, rather than being seen as a hindrance, to national development.

Purpose of the booklet

This booklet provides basic and practical information on multiple-use smallholder farm ponds. Its aim is to promote ponds as a diversification enterprise. It describes what should be considered to make pond-based farm enterprises successful and sustainable as a business. Information is provided on the role of organizations, public, private and donor, in promoting farm ponds, opportunities for and pitfalls to providing assistance, direct and indirect support required, and the strategic and technical challenges of making farmers self-reliant or at least less dependent. It suggests ways by which smallholder farmers can participate in the market economy through better market access and outlines strategies to attract the private sector to do business with them.

This Diversification booklet is not a 'how to' manual, numerous publications are available providing detailed farm pond rearing techniques, many of which are cited in the further reading section. This booklet is based on and is a continuation of the FAO publication 'Small ponds make a big difference', published in the year 2000.

Farm ponds
and livelihoods

Ponds add value to other farming activities: water from ponds can serve domestic and livestock water supplies as well as irrigation for high-value crops and vegetables. Farm ponds typically range from 30 m² to 500 m²; size depends on the resources of the farmer and larger natural 'small water bodies', like small lakes, can also be considered as farm ponds. Proximity of ponds to the farmer's house is vital for management and those which are fully integrated contribute most to the overall operation of the farm. Ponds *offer the opportunity to rear fish and* other aquatic organisms providing for diversification of farm enterprises and reduction of risk.

■ *Benefits to the household*

Nutrition
Water from ponds can provide irrigation for crops and water for livestock. This can have a positive effect on family nutrition, making crop and livestock production less risky and allowing families to have more farm products to consume. Fish can also be produced, providing for yet another important 'nutrient' in the family diet, as well as other aquatic organisms. Fish is an important source of protein for the family. Fish alleviates protein deficiency contributing to improved growth in children and helps them in their learning abilities, and fosters better health and less disease in the family. Although fish production from farm ponds may be limited, the ready availability of fish in small quantities allows families to easily catch a fish for a meal. With stocking of different sizes of fish and/or use of different *traditional fishing gear, harvests can* be fairly regular and consequently provide for a regular source of food.

Income
Although smallholders may not produce huge quantities of fish, yields are manageable and harvests are easy to process and store. However, smallholders rarely participate in formal markets and often barter their fish for other household needs. Barter, in effect, releases cash for other purchases.

Improved production techniques and better management practice can increase the production of fish from small farm ponds. With higher yields, supply to local markets can become an income generating activity for the household.

Added value

A well-managed integrated farm system comprising several enterprises including fish culture in ponds produces more products. The pond serves as a water storage structure and, as such, becomes a key asset of smallholder farms, supplying water to crops and animals. Crops can be integrated with the ponds in a multiple use system. Wastes accumulated in pond muds can be spread over gardens. Fish ponds in irrigation schemes add value to the scheme and serve as a back-up source of water when water shortage occurs or supply is temporarily cut off. There are mutual benefits to integrated and associated farming systems, such as wastes from gardens being fed to fish and water from ponds for irrigating the crops. Annex 1 provides examples of integration in Nigeria and Viet Nam and Figure 3 shows illustrations of upland and lowland models of integrated farming systems.

■ *Benefits to the community*

The community can benefit from the promotion of farm ponds in three ways:

1

It can draw more support from public agencies for rural infrastructure and services

Improved, as well as more efficient and sustainable, water use is one of the most important impacts of programmes promoting farm ponds. Improved smallholder livelihoods can lead to an increased pressure on public agencies to increase their support. Infrastructure development in these areas has generally been very slow. Participation in decision-making by the rural poor has been limited and local governments have been slow to improve infrastructure. However, when smallholders have a voice, and their farm production brings increased revenues to the communities, the people can begin to demand greater investments in infrastructure and services.

2

It can lead to farmer empowerment

There is need for political processes that ensure access and resolution of land tenure, property rights and water use issues. Resource use is a good introduction to a more active participation of people in the processes of policy formulation and development planning for rural areas. To better participate and have a stronger voice in these processes, farmers need to be organized and the association needs to be run professionally.

3
It generates employment

Smallholder fish production and related activities are carried out by family members using a largely non-cash system in which there is little need for capital. Thus the direct impact on formal employment is small. However, as production increases and farmers begin to link to markets and require more inputs than are available from the farm, more economic activities and jobs are generated in the community. These would range from production and supply of seed and feed and the processing and marketing of fish.

FIGURE 3   Integrated smallholder farming systems in lowland and upland environments illustrating the synergies among the different enterprises and the flow of materials and energy

Integrated farming system (lowland)

Integrated farming system (upland)

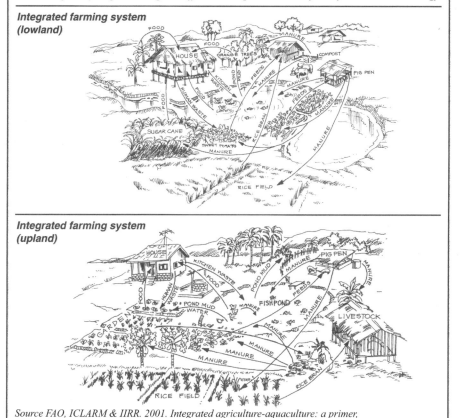

Source FAO, ICLARM & IIRR. 2001. Integrated agriculture-aquaculture: a primer, FAO Fisheries Technical Paper No.407, Rome.

The contribution of fish
and other aquatic organisms to livelihoods

Raising fish is an obvious use for a farm pond; fish adds value to the water. From a farming systems standpoint, fish converts otherwise agricultural and household waste into food when used as feed. To the household, fish adds to the basket of goods produced on the farm. It diversifies the livelihood options and, as an additional enterprise, serves as a fallback – for food or for cash – if other enterprises provide low yields or fail. However, it does add to the complexity of farm management and therefore can increase risks.

Other than finfish, farm ponds can be stocked with the high value freshwater prawn (*Macrobrachium* spp). Seed can be taken from the wild. But if common carps or catfish, which can prey on small crustaceans, are also grown, the prawn seed would have to be stocked ahead and allowed to grow bigger before carps or catfish are stocked. But freshwater prawn is a carnivore and, as in Bangladesh, they are fed with snails. They are grown in rice paddies. In Thailand, they are raised in monoculture and fed with formulated feed. It can be a difficult crop to grow and can complicate pond management.

Edible aquatic plants can also be grown on the edges of the pond. In East and Southeast Asia, probably the most popular edible aquatic plant is *Ipomoea aquatica,* a semi-aquatic tropical plant grown as a leaf vegetable. Common names include water spinach, swamp cabbage, water convolvulus, water morning-glory, *kangkung* in Indonesian, *pak boong* in Thailand. It flourishes in waterways and hardly requires care. It is used in Malay and Chinese cuisine, especially in rural areas. It has also been introduced to the United States of America where its high growth rate caused it to become an environmental problem. The plant is similar to spinach in its nutritional benefits. It is not known if this plant has been introduced in Africa but there might be some equivalent plants that can be grown in ponds or other species such as water chestnut.

The long experience from aquaculture in Asia offers models in small-scale fish husbandry practices for other regions. An important lesson from the Asian models is that fish farming is effectively integrated with surrounding activities and can be seen as one of several part-time occupations that are undertaken with little dependence from government support, as noted by the United Nations Development Programme (UNDP) in 1987: *"Traditional Asian aquaculture is self-reliant and low cost, representing an ideal for aquaculture elsewhere in the developing world"*.

Previously in Asia, with the many rivers, lakes, irrigation channels, man-made reservoirs and often the proximity of a sea, people needed only to catch fish for the family's lunch or dinner; they did not have to dig ponds or set up cages and pens to produce fish for home consumption. Subsequently, with the marked reduction of these natural resources and population growth, Asian small farms were driven by the desire to earn income: they produce fish for the household and for sale. This commercial orientation of smallholder farms raises another set of issues. Most smallholder farmers have a poor understanding of the market; lack the collective strength for more bargaining power; and have limited awareness of modern food safety and production standards. With little experience, information and organization, they have no basis on which to access modern market chains for their products.

The opportunity for development assistance can thus expand to include enabling smallholder farmers to access markets and adopt more productive and sustainable farming practices.

■ *Farming strategies*

A number of farming systems have been developed to enable smallholder farmers to make optimum use of their limited resources and be more productive. Some farmers can integrate fish farming with other on-farm activities such as crops and animal husbandries. This integration involves cost savings through use of resources over several enterprises not to mention the advantage of having multiple-use, water-harvesting and storage facilities on a farm that improve returns to land and labour. Beneficial associations are another possibility with small ponds linked to the raising of vegetables and/or livestock. On-farm water reservoirs are important to soil conservation and in sustaining other agricultural activities. In this regard, small ponds can play a major role.

Integrated small-scale fish farming creates value in the market chain. An example of a self-reliant and sustainable model that highlights the central role of a small farm pond in integrated farming is the VAC system in Viet Nam. It is a commercially oriented enterprise; the objective of

FIGURE 4   *A fish farm in Lao PDR with integrated rice and fish culture that shows animal pens built over the water in order that ducks will fertilize the ponds*
(Photo: © FAO/20910/K. Pratt)

the farm family is to earn income on top of producing its own food, particularly rice and fish which are Asian staples (see Annex 1).

■ *Market potential*
Post-harvest loss of fish is a major concern; it can be 30 percent or higher. Solutions to this have always been difficult given the warm climate, shortage of ice or lack of cold storage facilities, and poor handling and processing techniques found in many countries. Promoting good post-harvest practices through training and building on local traditions can be an effective way of reducing post-harvest losses.

Population growth in general and the rapid growth of urban centres, coupled with the decline of capture fisheries have increased demand for farmed fish. In a number of countries, demand is often met by imports. This approach harms the domestic economy by virtually paying for foreign labour encapsulated into the imported goods and spending foreign exchange, which could very well be spent for improved

FIGURE 5   A group of farmers dividing their fish harvest; some to be sold in the market and some for processing
(Photo: © FAO/22325/A. Proto)

rural infrastructure and services to smallholder farmers. It is advisable thus to promote fish farming.

A crucial requirement for being able to sell fish, other than easy access to a market through proximity or a good transport system, is the volume and reliability of supply of marketable fish. This implies forming a cluster of small farmers who are able to harvest regularly a volume of marketable fish that buyers find worthwhile to collect or which farmers themselves can bring to market.

Smallholder fish production systems

Good fish production in farm ponds begins with the selection of type of pond system that is most compatible with prevailing conditions. It is necessary to be aware of the local traditional and agricultural calendars in order to organize farm pond labour as well as harvests. As populations grow, pressure on land and water resources increase and conflicts regarding access to and use of resources occur. These issues may also relate to the proximity of the farm pond to the farmer's core farm activities. Legal and social issues regarding small ponds include property rights, water rights and crop losses from poaching. Farm ponds isolated from the core farm often have unclear property rights and poaching can be a problem. Clearly it is easier to assist farmers having all activities in one location.

■ *Types of farm pond systems*
Fish farming at the smallholder level could involve eight different types of farm pond systems: **1** runoff ponds, **2** ground-water ponds, **3** borrow pit ponds, **4** derivation ponds, **5** ponds using siphoned or pumped water, **6** rice paddies, **7** ponds integrated in irrigation schemes and **8** small water bodies.

Ponds may vary in depth, but better production is obtained in ponds having a depth of at least 1.2 m and shallows at 0.3 m. This helps limit encroachment of aquatic vegetation as ponds with greater shallows may suffer from uncontrollable weed problems, which actually limit fish production.

1 Runoff ponds
Runoff ponds are built in the watershed and receive water from rainfall, thus being entirely controlled by climate. These ponds are often located near the top of watersheds, where the water catchment area is limited, as they could be washed out when there are heavy rains if located low in the watershed. Sites for the dam should be chosen at the head of a shallow valley or between two small hills. Such ponds receive varying quantities of runoff depending on the ground cover. Forests have lower runoff than open areas or farmed fields. Such ponds play multiple roles in soil conservation, water harvesting

and food production. Runoff ponds require a spillway or overflow system. Information is available to determine the watershed-pond ratio, the size of overflow systems based on watershed ground cover and surface area. Siphons may be used in some of these ponds to draw water for irrigation or for additional ponds at the base of the dam. Since they rely on rainfall and lack a permanent water source, runoff ponds may need to be harvested before the water level drops so low as to allow heavy predation by birds and animals.

Advantages

Runoff ponds take advantage of rainfall that otherwise would flow as runoff water.

Disadvantages

Water supply can be erratic. These ponds may dry up in the dry season and thus require close management to produce a crop of fish. During a heavy rain there is risk of dams being flooded and washed out if spillways or overflows are insufficient in size for the area of the watershed. Runoff ponds may suffer high loss of fish

FIGURE 6   *Ground water ponds*
(Photo: © FAO/20903/K. Pratt)

from poaching and have unclear land tenure issues. They are prone to siltation.

Management

Since the cropping cycle is short, runoff ponds should be stocked with large juvenile fish if a large size fish is desired at harvest. Nutrients added to these ponds become concentrated as water volume decreases, but this may enhance fish production. Nutrients may be lost when the dams spill.

2 Ground water ponds

These are dug in low-lying areas where the water table is near the surface. Flooding is a threat and can be avoided by building a canal around the pond to divert water. Control of these ponds is difficult, as their water volume is dictated by the ground-water level. It may not be possible to drain such ponds, and complete harvest of the fish is difficult unless the water is pumped out. The bottom of the pond cannot be dried. However, fish can be harvested by hook and line on a regular basis or by the use of other common fishing gear. It is not always necessary to drain a pond for harvesting as fish can be caught by other means and the storage of water may be more important to the whole farm than the value of the fish. During droughts, the level of ground water may drop, lowering the level of

water in these ponds. In such cases, if the owner has no possibility of topping up the water from a stream or a pump, he or she may have to fish out the pond before it dries up.

Advantages

Ground water ponds take advantage of low-lying areas having 'high' water tables just beneath the ground surface.

Disadvantages

The ground water level may fluctuate during the year causing ponds to flood or dry up. These ponds require close management to produce a crop of fish in such conditions. Often ground water ponds cannot be drained, although families have been seen to empty the water with buckets. As noted above, farmers may prefer to maintain the pond water for its multiple use on the farm. Since such ponds can be isolated, marshy or swampy areas, they may be difficult to access, have limited agricultural use and can be subject to poaching and predation. If the ponds have frequent water exchange, it may not be possible to increase water productivity through fertilization. Unclear land tenure issues complicate use of such ponds.

Management

Ground water ponds that have big fluctuations in water level as the dry season advances, may need to be stocked with large juvenile fish if a large size fish is desired at harvest. Nutrients added to these ponds may become concentrated as water volume decreases, but this may enhance fish production. Care is taken not to make the water eutrophic (excessive algal bloom from too much fertility, which then exhausts the oxygen) with an overload of nutrient.

3 Borrow-pit ponds

Borrow-pit ponds are created through road construction, from the holes dug in making mud bricks, or in other circumstances when the by-product of an activity is a hole in the ground. These ponds may have uneven bottoms and rough shapes and require some work to make them more manageable for fish production. Some borrow-pits may be very shallow while others may be very deep and hazardous to children and others who may not know how to swim. Such ponds may be managed by individuals or as groups, these ponds being labour intensive. These ponds may be filled with water through runoff or through ground water, or both. Borrow-pit ponds may be seasonal. If an alternative source of water is not available, such ponds must be monitored closely to arrange a harvest of the fish before the water level drops too low.

Advantages

Borrow-pit ponds take advantage of holes made in the ground as a by-product of other activities. Turning them into fish ponds makes them valuable.

Disadvantages

Water supply may vary considerably in pits, with water loss in dry periods. These may dry up entirely in the dry season and thus require close management to produce a crop of fish. Land tenure may be a problem and pit ponds may need to be operated by a group when perceived as having common ownership.

Management

Borrow-pit ponds may only be seasonal and could hold water four to six months of the year. Therefore, they may need to be stocked with larger fish. Nutrients added to these ponds may become concentrated as water volume decreases, but this may also enhance fish production. Care is taken not to make the water eutrophic (excessive algal bloom from too much fertility, which then exhausts the oxygen) with an overload of nutrients.

4 Derivation ponds

Ponds supplied with water by derivation canal are perhaps the easiest to manage. These can be filled

FIGURE 7   Ponds supplied with water through a derivation canal
(Photo: © FAO/12738/E. Errath)

or drained at any time. Such ponds are built near a stream or other source of water, out of a flood zone. A water supply canal is dug or a structure is put in place to bring water to the ponds. Water conveyance structures can be made of bamboo, roofing sheets, tiles, stones or a variety of other readily available materials. This type of pond can be built by hand labour in areas with gentle slopes. It is best to select sites where 'cut equals fill'; where the earth to be dug equals the fill dirt required to build the dikes. Obviously this results in cost savings as ponds of the same area that are entirely 'dug' require roughly double the labour of 'cut equals fill' ponds. For example, a 100 m² dug pond would require 70 m³ or more of earth work assuming a sloping bottom, whereas a 'cut equals fill' pond would require half or less the earthwork, depending on the slope of the land. In open areas, a labourer can usually dig 1 m³ of earth a day.

Advantages

Derivation ponds take advantage of the presence of streams which, because of their fall in elevation (topography), can be diverted into a canal which can supply water to fish ponds out of a flood zone. Such ponds are usually the most efficient and least costly to build as their topography lends itself to earth work where 'cut equals fill'.

Disadvantages

Water canals require an understanding of topography and some skill in construction. It is necessary to follow a 'contour line' at the same elevation, allowing for a slight slope for the water to slowly move through the canal. Sometimes the soils along the area of the canal are porous and not water-retaining, leading to some loss of water.

Management

Derivation ponds are usually fully controllable by the farmer who may fill or drain such a pond anytime. Nutrients added to these ponds are usually well-exploited for fish production.

5 Siphon or pump filled ponds

Smallholders use water from their ponds to support the entire farm. If a farmer has land with a topography suitable for having pond(s) at higher elevations on the farm, water can be siphoned from the pond to irrigate lower-level crops. Such strategically located ponds provide a farmer with a convenient farm layout. Siphons are commonly used in irrigation schemes to move water from the water supply canals to the fields. Likewise siphons can be used between ponds built in tandem down small valleys. But if the farmer has ponds on the lower elevations of the farm, pumping would be required for irrigation. Waters from these low-lying ponds can be pumped up to the top of the farm for reuse in conservation management. Treadle pumps could be used for this purpose.

Advantages

Ponds filled with siphoned or pumped water take advantage of waters that otherwise would not be recycled without use of siphons or pumps. Siphons are cheap and many farmers use plastic pipes in moving water from one place to another. With a centrally located pond, a siphon or treadle pump can be used to fill it anytime of the day.

Disadvantages

Siphoned or pumped waters require effort to manage and close supervision to maintain desirable water levels. It is necessary to invest in siphons and a treadle or mechanical pump. Motor pumps may not be economical as they require fuel and maintenance not to mention the initial cash outlay.

Management

Siphon or pumped water ponds can be filled or drained anytime. Nutrients added to these ponds are usually well-exploited for fish production. Ponds filled via siphon or pump, take advantage of the presence of other ponds, water bodies or streams located beside the farm pond.

6 Rice paddies

Rice paddies may also produce fish and have been shown to produce 10 percent higher rice yields and as much as 50 percent increased income through sale of fish in comparison to a mono crop of rice. Fish integrated with rice farming has helped many farmers in Asia greatly increase their income; however adoption of this rice-fish integration has been slow in Africa, except in Madagascar where it has met with success. The longer-stemmed rice, with longer growing season, is more suitable for rice-cum-fish production as it allows deeper water in the paddy and a growing period that produces larger size fish. This is the case in many areas of Madagascar as they grow only one crop of rice a year. Elsewhere, short-stemmed rice with a shorter growing period is used to harvest two or more crops a year. This allows a three- to four-month growing season for fish and may only produce small fish. This does allow for rice paddies to be used for fingerling production for sale or exchange with other farmers. This

FIGURE 8 A rice paddy with fish farming
(Photo: © FAO/20905/K. Pratt)

Farm ponds for water, fish and livelihoods

may satisfy the needs of smallholder farmers, but other farmers who prefer larger fish would want to plant a rice variety with a longer maturity period.

Advantages

Rice paddy ponds produce a 'balanced meal of rice and fish'. It has a high production and returns per unit area. Rice paddies modified for rearing fish have stronger dikes as a result of digging 'refuge canals' for the fish. Long-stemmed rice with longer growing season (i.e. more than five months) favours integration with fish.

Disadvantages

Rice paddies must be modified to provide a deeper 'refuge canal' to protect fish from predation and high water temperatures. Most rice farmers prefer to grow rice only rather than integrate rice with fish. Short stemmed rice and the improved varieties of rice with short growing periods call for shallow waters and a short growing season of only 3 to 4 months. Additionally, use of pesticides and herbicides is not favourable for fish production. Poaching is sometimes a problem.

Management

Rice paddy ponds require close management as regards the timing of stocking of juvenile fish. Water management is crucial so that the fish can grow to a good size.

7 Integrated irrigation aquaculture ponds

Some smallholder farmers may have ponds located within irrigation schemes. They can benefit from the system of water supply canals. Most irrigation schemes target a

---

CASE STUDY 1 Raising fish in rice paddies in Nigeria

Rice-cum-fish farming has been exploited for many years in Asia and now this integrated farming is starting to be practiced by smallholder farmers in Africa. Nigeria's Government has expressed a lot of interest in rice/fish farming as it offers a way to reduce imports of rice (1.8 metric tonnes(MT)/year) and fish (700 000 MT/year). This could also create employment in rural areas and reduce poverty. Research in Nigeria at the National Cereals Research Institute (NCRI) has shown an increase of 54 percent in revenues with rice/fish production as compared to rice production only. Presence of fish in rice paddies adapted with a refuge canal yielded up to a 15 percent increase in rice production. In small plots, Nigerian smallholder farmers have produced up to 3.2 tonnes of rice per hectare and as much as 480 kilograms of fish per hectare. Rice farmers in the flood zone, in the south eastern part of the country, borrowed fish nets to fence off their rice paddies before harvest and were able to harvest up to 90 kilograms of wild fish that grew in the rice paddy.

particular crop and some areas within the scheme may not be suitable for crop production. These areas maybe suited for building ponds. Fish ponds increase the efficiency of land use within the irrigation domain and the presence of fish ponds adds to the variety of crops produced. Use of irrigation aquaculture could include rice-fish farming, rotation of crops with fish, as well as ponds integrated with gardens. Ponds could be built uphill from crops and provide siphoned water to irrigate the crops, or ponds could be downhill from the irrigated crops, which would require pumping back the water to the crest of the system for multiple water use.

Advantages

Ponds integrated in irrigation schemes add value to the irrigation water. They diversify production in irrigation schemes, which often are constructed at high cost to produce only one crop. Such ponds can be built in areas within the irrigation scheme that are unsuitable for crops. Ponds could also produce fish which prey on the snails that in some places serve as vectors for bilharzia, the parasite frequently associated with irrigation schemes.

Disadvantages

Ponds need to be deeper than fields for crop production, so they can be drained completely by gravity flow,

otherwise a pump would be needed. Ponds built close to crop fields may receive pesticides and herbicides indirectly through wind movements, which could be detrimental to fish.

Management

Irrigation ponds can be filled or drained by the farmer. Nutrients added to these ponds are well-exploited for fish production.

8 Small water bodies

Some smallholders may have access to natural or man-made small water-bodies. These small water-bodies have multiple uses requiring multiple-use management that have to deal with common property and access rights. They are difficult to manage in traditional communities where contracts may be established by community leaders with nomadic fishermen who have little interest in sustaining its productivity. This can create conflicts with the resident fishermen and farmers. The community leaders should manage the use of these waters for the common good including small-scale irrigation, water harvesting and fishing.

Access to the fishery resource of small water bodies should be managed by the resident community members. Small water-bodies are usually sources of irrigation for nearby farm plots, and water for domestic

FIGURE 9 A small water body with a Peking duck enterprise, Zambia
(Photo: © FAO/14282/W. Gartung)

and livestock needs. Care must be made to avoid polluting the waters. A community management scheme, where responsibility of control and management rests with the members of the community should be agreed. The management arrangement would include stocking of fish, regulating fishing activities, enhancing its productivity and even using it for pen or cage culture of fish, as in Asia. This would need training to make people aware of the importance of managing this resource. Training and awareness-raising should aim at providing the co-management skills, culture-based fishery techniques and, probably the most important objective, instilling in the community a sense of collective ownership of the water body.

Integrated farm pond management and fish production systems

▪ *Water management*

All farm ponds serve as water storage for the farm. The pond site depends on a good water supply. Consideration needs to be taken on how the water enters the pond, how it is managed for fish production and used for maximum benefit to the farm.

The advantages of multiple use have already been described. To benefit from these advantages, the pond system must be planned and built well. Pond systems generally have an inlet and an outlet structure including a spillway or overflow for excess water. These structures can be of various designs and materials. They can be made from materials available on the farm or locally and should require no or very minimal cash outlay.

Ponds must be built from compacted soils with a proper design to avoid erosion, minimize maintenance and extend its life. The initial labour requirement to build a proper pond may be high, but a well-built pond will last a long time. A well-built pond for water storage would still require good maintenance; silt accumulates and vascular plants may encroach into the shallower parts. Ponds can become choked by aquatic plants such as water hyacinth. These plants, though, may have some use such as animal feed or organic fertilizer.

Some smallholder farmers may siphon water into the pond. Farmers may have access to treadle or mechanical pumps. Treadle pumps rely on foot power and cost much less to operate than mechanical pumps. Since treadle pumps are commonly used to irrigate gardens early and late in the day, a centrally located pond, filled by pumping could be used to store and hold water, allowing farmers to share pumps.

Most smallholders do not install drain pipes in their ponds, nor do they use pipes for entry of water, as they lack access to such resources. Instead of passing through an inlet pipe, water flows into the pond through an open canal. To drain ponds and harvest fish, most small pond owners simply dig a hole in the dike for the water to flow out. A filtering device is installed at the hole to hold the fish. It can be a basket, piece of netting or some fish-trap made of bamboo or

Farm ponds for water, fish and livelihoods

raffia. This allows the farmer to dry the pond and carry out maintenance before refilling.

Water management involves user management. If the water comes from a common source, the community can ration water use to individual farms and farm ponds. If the farm pond systems are communal property, as with a small water body, communal management is necessary. Community, group or joint management can be complicated.

■ *Obtaining seed*

Farm ponds used for raising fish may be stocked with a wide variety of fish or other aquatic organisms. Farm ponds, even if not used for managed fish production, should be stocked with fish anyway. Fish help control water-borne diseases, prey on mosquito larvae and some help control snails, which spread bilharzia.

Most farmers raise one or more of the many varieties of tilapias. Tilapias are indigenous in many parts of Africa and raised in most parts of the world. A major advantage of tilapias is that generally their seed is readily available, albeit of variable quality. Tilapias can spawn year round when conditions are suitable. Small adults or juveniles may be captured in the wild for stocking ponds. As tilapias spawn readily (usually after four months), seed may be obtained from a neighbour for the first stocking or from government or private suppliers. After the first stocking, the fish will spawn in the pond and the farmers can have a lot of small fish available for restocking after harvesting. However, as it is a very prolific fish, tilapia could over-populate a fishpond, producing progressively smaller fish if the pond is not drained and restocked. To help overcome this constraint, tilapias can be raised with a predator, such as catfish, to reduce the reproduction levels and further have catfish as a 'second crop'.

While tilapias remain popular among smallholder farmers, catfish farming has considerably increased, either in polyculture with tilapia or as a single crop. Seed are usually juvenile fish caught in the wild. Catfish tend to have specific spawning seasons linked to the rainy season when juveniles school and are easy to capture. Women and youth groups often catch juvenile catfish and tilapias for sale or barter to pond owners. Catfish are hardier than many of the species of farmed fish and can be stocked at higher densities than the tilapia. The decision as to which fish species to raise, depends on availability of fingerlings and the market. Because of the variable quality of seed, farmers should be trained to distinguish the good from the poor quality seed. This is a crucial

FIGURE 10 *Farmer in Honduras checking up on his brood fish*
(Photo: © FAO/18891/G. Bizzarri)

skill and should be an opportunity for farmers' training programmes. At the same time, efforts should be made to assist hatcheries, if seed supplies are from hatcheries, to produce quality seed.

Carps are another popular species for integrated or mono-culture in small farm ponds. They are hardy and prolific and grow fast with good feeding. There are several species (Chinese carps, Indian major carps, and common carps which includes the European carps). The common carps (*Cyprinus carpio*) would probably be the most suitable for small integrated farms because they breed well naturally. Brood stock can be collected from the wild or developed in the ponds. Common carp breeding can be carried out in *hapas* (inverted fine mesh nets) set in a pond. Other species such as the Indian major carps and Chinese carps would need a full hatchery facility, which requires a high capital investment. (A full hatchery consists of an elevated water tank, a source of good quality freshwater such as a tube well or a stream, circular spawning and breeding tank, hatching jar, holding tank, a shed for the whole structure except the elevated water tank, and brood fish tanks or pond).

This is an opportunity for assistance to small farmers. The expertise on brood stock rearing, breeding and hatchery acquired from working on common carps could be applied subsequently to other carp species or other freshwater fish species. It is also the foundation for improving quality of fish seed for small farms.

■ *Stocking*

Smallholders may obtain their initial fish seed from government or private fish hatcheries or other suppliers. But they may also produce their own fingerlings, barter seed from neighbour farmers, or catch from the wild. In choosing seed their needs to be a preference to use local and indigenous species.

Small ponds (of about 4 m^2 water surface area) are built beside the grow out ponds to hold small fish while pond preparation and cleaning is carried out. Once the main or grow-out pond is cleaned and refilled, these fish are transferred to it.

Organizations can play a role in identifying sources of reliable quality seed or securing initial seed as an entry point to supporting smallholder pond development. Care must be

FIGURE 11 When they reach the required size, small fish are transferred to larger ponds through sluices, Republic of Congo
(Photo: © FAO/11572/N. Brodeur)

taken in handling and stocking fish fingerlings. Transport and stocking must be done early in the day when the water is coolest. Fish should be counted at stocking. Poor handling and transport techniques stress the small fish and result in a lot of dead fish after stocking. Appropriate skills in these techniques need to be learned.

Where species are available, it may be good to raise two species of fish together in a pond. As mentioned above, a polyculture of the forage fish such as tilapia with the predator such as catfish can help produce larger fish, transforming many small tilapias into more desirable catfish. In such a polyculture, the forage fish (i.e. tilapia), is stocked ahead and allowed to grow a month or so, or when it starts reproducing, before stocking the predator. Small catfish are commonly stocked with tilapia in integrated poultry-cum-fish or pig-cum-fish farming systems resulting in higher productivity. Such integrated systems can only be done where there is good security and full-time surveillance is possible. As noted, it is best to have all smallholder farm activities at one core location.

Movement of live fish are subject to controls. There are regulations and protocols to comply with in moving fish between watersheds and across national borders. Farmers need to be made aware of the rules on movement and introduction of live fish. Development organizations can help farmers with compliance and assist governments in recording these movements.

■ *Fertilization*

Smallholders have limited resources, but most try to add nutrients to their ponds, such as farm and household by-products and some vegetable items for feed. The unrefined nature of these products causes them to serve more as fertilizers to enhance natural productivity, rather than as feed. Most of these items may be found near the ponds if the ponds are near the farm compound or farm plots. These materials tend to give a low fish yield. To compensate, subsistence farmers practice organic fertilization (with compost) to improve productivity. Dried grass and other plant material along with manure and other wastes are piled in a corner of the pond to dissolve and enhance natural productivity.

The effects of composting are manifested by green water colour indicating a 'bloom', dominated by phytoplankton. This provides natural fish food to filter feeding fishes such as tilapia. Farmers may also apply inorganic fertilizers and lime, but not all smallholders have the knowledge to calculate optimal applications.

Ponds that leak or have high flow-through may not be able to maintain a bloom and in such conditions, fish have little supplementary food. Farmers should learn to observe and interpret the behaviour of fish such as how they swim and respond to nutrient additions, on normal days, cloudy days, rainy days, cool days, and hot days. Careful observation can help farmers detect poor water quality, diseases and predation.

■ *Harvesting*
Smallholder fish production is variable and unpredictable. Most farm ponds however are likely to have yields that are twice the natural fish production in a natural water body. Production can range from 700 kg to 1 200 kg/ha/year. The quality and quantity of the harvest will depend on the farm system used and the management techniques employed. Regular cycles of stocking and harvesting; with harvesting accompanied by a complete draining and re-filling of the pond, often provide the highest yields. However, farmers with a 'water-first' set of priorities may be reluctant to drain ponds, while some farm ponds are difficult or impossible to drain. Thus, the decision of having complete or partial harvest is important. Farm ponds that are empty during certain periods of the year caused by seasonal water availability will, of course, have considerably lower yields.

■ *Processing*
On-farm or backyard fish processing is an opportunity for improving income by adding value to the fish as well as reducing wastage. As such, it is a good opportunity for introducing low-cost and easy to operate smoking, salting and drying techniques and training women in such techniques. Most traditional smoking methods usually rely on high temperatures over a short smoking time, producing poor quality fish charred on the outside and half-cooked inside. Such fish spoil easily.

A variety of fish smoking methods are available to small-scale rural farmers, from traditional 'alter smokers' to heavy smoking chambers made of welded metal. The output from traditional methods is small but uses a lot of fuel wood. It also carries a high risk of fire outbreak and may pose a health hazard, mainly to women and their children, who are typically responsible for processing. Some farmers may salt and dry fish. *Chorkor* (oven with trays) smoking kilns, designed in Ghana, have a high smoking capacity and are very well suited for backyard operation. The kiln can be made and easily repaired with locally available and low-cost materials.

FIGURE 12 Fish is smoked on a Chorkor
(Photo: © FAO/18298/P. Cenini)

In Asia, fish processing at the village level is either done by the farm household or a group of women who have acquired their own processing equipment. *Ikan kayu* (literally wooden fish because of its hard consistency) in Indonesia is a popular product form produced by women groups. It keeps well and fetches a good price. In Cambodia, drying and salting surplus freshwater fish is a backyard activity. Women have been taught by organizations, such as NGOs, improved techniques that preserve quality to assure a good product and do not involve the use of substances to ensure product safety.

■ *Marketing*

Smallholders usually market their own fish on the pond bank through barter or with sales to community members. Such farmers operate in an informal market system. Marketing of pond raised fish in a densely populated area may not be a problem. It would be more difficult if there is not much volume because farms are far and in between, harvests are not synchronized, and of course physical access to market is difficult. The market chain of smallholder farmers is much shorter than that of commercial farmers (refer back to Figure 2) and therefore the logistics may not be as difficult or costly. But if the objective is to enable small farmers to market in distant urban centres, then the value chain becomes longer and costs and risks increase.

The size of fish for market is also important. The preference of consumers is obviously the most important criterion. However, often it can be more profitable to sell smaller size fish on a per kilogram basis because the growing period is shorter and therefore turnover is faster. Even with the extra cost of seed for growing more than one crop, the annual return would still be higher. Generally, fish use feed more efficiently at the earlier stages of their growth.

FIGURE 13 *Choosing the right fish for marketing and fish to leave for further maturing*
(Photo: © FAO/22248/A. Proto)

Supporting fish ponds
as a diversification enterprise

Within the fisheries or agriculture sector, the role and contribution of farm ponds remain ill-defined. Few countries have aquaculture or agriculture strategies that specifically address the needs and define the impacts of farming systems that integrate small farm ponds; smallholders require interventions to respond to their long-term needs. Development of skills and changes in attitudes will usually require a few years. This situation sets the stage for the involvement of organizations, public, private and donor, for development assistance. An organization providing technical assistance to smallholder farmers needs to consider:

Assessment
of potentials and advice
Farmers that have ponds need an assessment of their pond's production history, present status and potentials. Some may only need short-term support, and follow-up for monitoring production. Farmers who would like to build new ponds need more long-term input for assessing their conditions and the potential for farm ponds.

Collaboration
Organizations need to link together with programmes in research and extension, so that technology provision and extension services will continue once development projects have finished. Extension materials such as newsletters, technical notes, brief fact sheets and radio programmes may already exist, but if they do not they should be developed. NGOs could work with government researchers and extension workers to produce credible and easy to understand extension materials. It may be necessary to help build local government capacity for outreach, which could include training of field personnel.

Training
Among smallholders, management practices and techniques of integrated farming can be the core subjects of training and study visits programmes. Integrated farming is more complicated than mono crop farming so that hands-on training combined with demonstration would be effective approaches. Farmer field schools (FFSs) are cost effective,

provide training based on 'learning by doing', follow the seasonal schedule, bring farmers together in groups and encourage them to learn from each other.

Helping farmers organize properly and for the right reasons

When efforts are clearly rewarded it is easier to promote the adoption of a new technology or practice. A community management approach in effect pools and shares resources for collective benefit. But there will always be some free riders, or individuals who would want to benefit from the results without contributing much or at all to the effort. Individual farm operations of organized farmers would likely be a better approach than communal or group management. Organized farmers individually operating their own farms would still have the combined strength of transacting with suppliers or buyers, helping each other, or pooling their harvest for more cost-effective marketing without the burden of suspecting who might be gaining benefits that are disproportionate to his/her contribution to the pooled effort. Communal and cooperative management would apply better to small water bodies with no individual ownership.

Specific assistance and interventions are described next.

Organizations could structure their inputs around a core framework for assisting farm pond programmes through the following activities:

■ *Feasibility*

Past programmes tended to promote the construction of ponds without proper assessment of site and area suitability. To avoid repeating this mistake, it would be useful to run a checklist of questions. The answers would provide information on whether it is an appropriate project and if so how to promote, develop, and possibly upgrade farm ponds and smallholder fish farming in an area. A checklist of questions is provided.

1 Are there farm ponds in the area of interest?
2 Is there a desire by the people to use these and/or build new ponds?
3 What are the resources available locally?
4 Are there available local skills in fish farming?
5 What is needed to put farm ponds to sustainable use?
6 Are there means to realistically and sustainability meet these needs?

If the answer to either question 2, 4 or 6 are 'No', there is no sufficient justification to promote farm ponds in the area. Otherwise, proceed with the next set of questions:

7 What types of small ponds are found in the area?

8 Who owns the small ponds? Describe the typical farmer owning the ponds?

9 Where are small ponds likely to be located?

10 What interventions can an organization provide to best assist smallholder farmers with ponds?

11 How would an organization's assistance to smallholder farmers with ponds impact the community?

12 What types of training are needed for small farmers to effectively manage small ponds?

13 How are inputs provided and products marketed? What does the value chain look like for smallholder farmers with ponds?

14 What species and volume of production are possible with the small ponds?

15 What are the nearby sources of information, technology and advice available for farmers?

A more extensive checklist is provided in annex 2.

Suitable conditions for farm ponds include an adequate quantity of good quality water and land with water-retaining soils. Climate plays a role in management of ponds as cool temperatures, flooding or drought pose risks that need to be mitigated by good management. Pond construction requires skilled labour. Seasonal availability of labour is a consideration because construction of ponds needs to be done during the off season for major crops to avoid competition; more skilled labour for pond management is also required. Management and security of the crop becomes critical if the pond is far from the family compound. Access and a secured entitlement to the land and water resources are essential conditions.

■ *Practical training*

Farmers that already have farm ponds and those who would like to build ponds require different types of training. A number of those with ponds may be too isolated or in situations where it is difficult to help them technically. Poorly located and poorly built ponds are perhaps beyond help. It would be cheaper to build a new pond than to rehabilitate one that has been badly built. Organizations need to carefully determine the kind of assistance to farmers having old farm ponds. These ponds may be expensive or nearly impossible to renovate. On the other hand, farmers, in the absence of any external assistance, may have

FIGURE 14 *A fish culture extension agent introducing the basics of fish farming in a village*
(Photo: © FAO/14929/R. Cannarsa)

FIGURE 15 *A practical fish farming demonstration*
(Photo: © FAO/16162/U. Nermark)

developed 'management' practices to make the pond fit into the farming system so that that new inputs might upset this equilibrium.

A geographic concentration of older ponds can be better managed and assisted, if not by improving the structures by improving the access to inputs including information and market. Training of groups should be conducted at a smallholder farm under actual conditions. This training can be short- or medium-term with modest financial investment. Support to new entrants requires a more comprehensive approach for both pond construction and fish production. Ponds are more complex than holes in the ground; they consist of dikes, a filtered water entry and a drain. Training and support activities aimed at this group require more money and time as well as a high level of technical skill on the part of the service provider.

Short-term training can target a specific area where there is considerable value-added for farm pond operators. Such short-courses could deal with: procurement, handling and transport of fish seed; water harvesting technologies; fish harvesting techniques; crop storage; control and use of aquatic vegetation. Longer-term interventions provide support to strengthen extension services. NGOs could provide this service or partner with other public institutions in the service area. Rural smallholder farmers need trainers experienced in fish culture. Staff in some countries are gaining practical experience and greatly increasing their capacity to serve as facilitators in Farmer Field Schools (FFSs). Programmes can be established for training fisheries graduates at private fish farms.

■ *Farmer groups*
Some smallholders participate in organizations which seek to support improved services for farmers. At the smallholder level, such organizations may be traditional farmers' organizations and can be a voice for improved government extension support. In most cases, smallholders are often too poor or isolated to join associations. Still, such groups could help develop smallholder farms. Training of groups on technical and management matters can help smallholder farmers. Further grouping farmers together may provide a forum for 'voicing' issues, such as improved infrastructure. Associating farmers into groups can be a catalyst for fishpond development and local community development .

There are pitfalls to organizing or promoting the organization of farmers. The first is associating or joining a group for the wrong reason.

Farmers have formed associations not from a desire to join together for fish production but to get a loan or some gratuity from the government or assistance organization (Moehl *et al.*, 2006). On the other hand, a functional grouping of farmers can serve valuable purposes. But farmers need to be helped to organize only when they see the need and decide on it for their own reasons rather than be told to do so. If and when they do, assistance could be provided to improve their knowledge and skill to professionally manage the association. Working with organized farmers will make it easier and cheaper to provide services and hasten the transfer of technology. An association or group with a few progressive members would likely function more effectively. The progressive members could serve as examples or even advisers to others. Farmer-to-farmer training is not only inexpensive; it is usually more effective because of the credibility of a fellow farmer who is clearly successful.

■ *Gender*

Women have always played a prominent role in farming. Training programmes for women and projects promoting them as equal partners in development that include health care

FIGURE 16 *A Farmer group harvesting fish and sorting by size for marketing*
(Photo: © FAO/14929/R. Cannarsa)

FIGURE 17 *Women feeding fish for market in a small water body*
(Photo: © FAO/21697/A. Proto)

FIGURE 18 *Transporting fish in ice boxes to market*
(Photo: © FAO/21194/A. Proto)

issues have proven their value with relatively quick implementation of innovations.

■ *Role definition*

A strategic plan to develop the smallholder fish farming sector includes a clearer definition of the roles of government, NGOs and the private sector. This would avoid inefficiencies and duplication of efforts, which usually happen when responsibilities are ill-defined, roles are unclear and objectives are ambiguous. With limited resources, there is general consensus on the need to define the roles and responsibilities of different development partners.

Organizations, like NGOs, too often have pursued their own programmes without meshing them with that of the government and others. Resources are thus wasted from redundancy of efforts and farmers get confused from a multiplicity of programmes. A national strategy can clearly define interventions and assure that all areas of need are being addressed. An overview of broad and specific services and responsibilities between the public and private sectors is provided in Table 1.

In a multi-stakeholder participation and democratic environment, government is only one of the stakeholders in decision-making. The

FIGURE 19 *Woman selling fish from her own market stall*
(Photo: © FAO/21190/A. Proto)

increasing shift towards a market economy can enable governments to lighten themselves of the burden of providing public employment to focus more effectively on its role as a regulator, promoter of development initiatives, and facilitator of activities for the private sector. Development agencies can contribute to these by, on the one hand, partnering the government in performing these roles and, on the other hand, helping the farmers gain strength and the ability to demand that these roles be indeed performed by government. Strengthening of farmer groups should also make them more responsible farmers and a strong partner of government instead of being perennially dependent on government assistance.

Governments are increasingly aware of the advantages of national and intra-regional networking for information exchange and the introduction of proven technologies from other sectors and countries. This avoids having to spend unnecessarily for research and technology development on something already available. Development assistance organizations, sometimes with their own contacts and networking, can help strengthen and widen the linkages formed by governments with external sources of expertise and information.

TABLE 1   Overview of services and responsibilities from the public and private sector in assisting smallholder farmers

	Service provision	Responsibilitie	Funding	Oversight	Comments
1	Broodfish management	Public	Public	Public/private	Possibility of using public facilities.
2	Fish seed	Private	Private	Public/private	Quality seed starting to be available to some farm pond operators; segmentation of operations into hatchery, nursery and grow-out increases technical efficiencies and creates more employment.
3	Fish feeds	Private	Private	Farmers and feed industry	Farm pond operators most often source own feeds. Quality improvement needed. Advice based on economics of feeding needed.
4	Advisory services (outreach)	Public/private partnership	Public/private partnership	Public/private/ professional associations	Some group could certify qualifications of advisors.
5	Fish processing & marketing standards	Public/private	Public/private partnership	Public/private	Control and monitor both input/output quality & food safety
6	Environmental and quality monitoring	Public	Public/private partnership	Public/private	Few exist or are applied. Much improvement needed.
7	Research	Public	Public/private partnership	Public/private	Relevance of research enhanced with government-private sector-farmer group dialogues
8	Education & training	Public/private	Public/private partnership	Public/private	Government improves standards and capacities
9	Infrastructure	Public/some private	Public/private partnership	Public	Roads & market infrastructures
10	Input supplies	Private	Public/private partnership	Private with public monitoring	Quality & safety assurance; advice on cost-effective use of inputs

▣ *Enabling environment*

An important role of government is to improve the enabling environment for the development of smallholder farming. The principal instrument to achieve this aim is a strategic plan for the sector. The major components of the plan that would provide a favourable environment for development includes:

Public investment

Investments into the sector would be helped by a higher profile, but information is very limited or totally lacking on smallholders and their output. Generally statistical services have not been able to gather accurate data on fish production from smallholders because of various constraints and the fact that smallholder farmers' economic outputs are hardly accounted for. With the lack of, or limited information available on rural smallholder farm ponds, their contribution is under-reported and their potential for business and government investment not known.

There are many public agencies and institutions other than the ministry responsible for fisheries or aquaculture that should be involved in farm pond development programmes. These include environmental, water affairs, research, education, health, social affairs, public works, cooperative and statistics agencies. They can propose or develop assistance for farm ponds in line with their institutional mandates, as for instance, flood and erosion control, training and education, water supply regulations, farm-to-market roads, market infrastructures, environmental safeguards, and health and welfare. Their roles and services will need to be synchronized, which underlines the importance of a strategic plan for the development of the smallholder farming sector. The strategy would serve to provide coherence to the policies and activities of the different government agencies involved in rural development. There is an obvious need to have one harmonized farm pond programme, with government playing a coordinating role with development partners.

Government can organize support to smallholders through meetings with stakeholders and organizations to reach consensus on areas of intervention; this needs to be closely monitored by government. There is need for government to create links between research, education and advisory services. Government can bring the stakeholders to agreement to avoid duplicating efforts. This coordination task can be facilitated by establishing a national aquaculture task force, composed of all stakeholder group representatives.

Farm ponds for water, fish and livelihoods

41

Financial services

While some smallholder farmers can benefit from credit schemes, they generally are so isolated they lack access to microcredit. Nevertheless, recent years have seen impressive growth in the provision of microcredit. Organizations could facilitate access for smallholder farm pond programmes. Microcredit funds would be most appropriate for one-off expenditures such as purchasing the initial stock of fish or employing additional labour to complete pond facilities. There is a variety of community institutions that have traditionally assisted in providing cash and other resources to members, often on a rotational basis. These structures should, as appropriate, be mobilized to assist farm pond programmes.

It is important to differentiate loans from grants. Decades of experience have demonstrated that gratuities are counter-productive; they foster dependence. The past decades of neglect have demonstrated that smallholders can build and keep farm ponds with no external support and no gifts. Improvements can be achieved with the provision of high quality technical support and not by free wheelbarrows, seed, feed or fertilizer.

Policy and regulations

Although smallholders have long been outside the main policy and regulatory mainstream, the situation is changing. Some governments are proposing the need for licenses for farm ponds and water uptake and discharge. Others are suggesting the need for environmental impact assessments (EIAs) for structures such as farm ponds. There are related and potentially regulated concerns such as watershed management, water-borne disease control, conservation areas, and other concerns. Organizations can serve as an interface for the smallholder and regulatory agencies, provide awareness training and prepare simple booklets to advise on compliance with various regulations. Similar processes also help farmers contribute to policy and regulation activities by seeking their feedback and assessment of what works and what is counterproductive.

Participation of all stakeholders would go a long way in enabling policy and regulations on rural agriculture and fish production. Crucial issues that policy and regulations need to address include licensing, water use rights, land tenure, movement of products, biodiversity and environmental concerns.

By working with farmers' associations it is possible to enforce some regulations through members and to protect their growing industry. Through such a mechanism, the public sector can play a role in enforcement via community-based programmes. With reasonable government regulations developed through inclusive participation of stakeholders, farmer groups can receive training where they are shown the need to embrace such regulations and thus become partners with government in enforcement.

Opportunities and challenges

Aquaculture has been a rapidly growing economic activity and smallholder farmers can benefit from this momentum with improved services. As the momentum builds, institutions and organizations can use these forces to ensure that farm pond programmes are catered for and receive increased support. Diversification of livelihoods for smallholders that includes farm ponds involves a process, which should include: integration of water supply to the farm, understanding local knowledge of integrated farming with several farm enterprises, and understanding the farmer's circumstances and capabilities in order for him or her to get the highest possible benefit from the integration, while minimizing the risks of failure.

The multiple use of water from ponds needs to be well understood in order that it can be optimally used to produce farm products and meet domestic needs. The benefits from the presence of water could exceed the benefits from fish production alone.

Organizations should also try to collaborate and work with women farmers. The number of women who are involved in farming is increasing. Training can be developed to suit their needs and adjusted to their circumstances. Opportunities exist to promote the organization of farmers and strengthen their capacity to manage the association and manage community development projects. All these would open further opportunities to the entire farming community such as attracting business investments and more government support. In summary, development of farm ponds has the potential to improve economic growth in rural areas through increased on-farm employment, increased agricultural production, provision of quality food, generating more household income, and improved food security.

However, providing assistance to smallholders with ponds is fraught with many constraints. The basic farmer capacity and resource constraints can be dealt with through:

- improved understanding of the possible contributions of farm ponds, including when they are appropriate and when they are not;

Farm ponds for water, fish and livelihoods

- advice on more effective use of resources of smallholder farms;
- guidance for maximizing production from input of nutrients to the ponds;
- strategies and techniques to optimize overall farm production;
- training programmes for both technical and management support;
- training to improve the capacities of farmer organizations;
- improved rural outreach;
- improved institutional support services, access to inputs and to markets;
- improved transport and post-harvest handling for fish;
- research that is demand-driven;
- articulation of a National Aquaculture Development Strategy that includes support to small farmers.

Organizations should seek balance between promoting smallholder fish production and attaining food security and improved livelihoods. Many opportunities exist for helping smallholder farmers achieve higher harvests and better economic returns from the integration of farm ponds.

Annex 1

Examples of integrated fish farming: Nigeria and Viet Nam

Integrated fish farming in Nigeria

An inventory of 2 600 private fish farms in Nigeria revealed that 50 percent of fish farmers integrate poultry, piggery or livestock with their fish production; additionally integrated crop farming and rice/fish farming is also on the increase. Fish farming integrated with other animal production was adapted in Nigeria to reduce feeding and labour costs and began perhaps with the difficulties in finding fish feeds by smallholder farmers. Integrated fish farming involves planting shallow-rooted crops on dikes or rearing animals in pens beside or over the fishponds where the wastes are allowed to enter the pond to be recycled as organic fertilization for increased production of natural fish foods. This method has been used in Asia for centuries.

Smallholder fish farmers have relied on integrated fish farming for supply of feed inputs to their fish for many years. Through diversification of farm enterprises such as field crops, vegetable gardens, poultry and some small ruminant livestock as well as one or more fishponds to sustain their families, farmers spread out their risk, lower costs, and increase income spread out over the year.

VAC or 'garden-fishpond-livestock' integration in Viet Nam

Integrated farming in a relatively small plot of farm land is a traditional approach to family food production in the poor, rural regions of Viet Nam. The integration of the home lot, garden, livestock and fishpond is called the VAC system (VAC in Vietnamese is *vuon, ao, chuong* which means garden/pond/livestock pen). The widespread promotion of the VAC system known as the VAC movement began in the early 1980s. The objective of the movement was to increase and stabilize the nutritional standard of the rural poor.

This farming system is family-managed, with practically all labour coming from the household. VAC farms can be found in various agro-ecological conditions, including irrigated lowlands, rainfed uplands and peri-urban areas. Ponds are usually constructed when the farmer needs to fill up an area of

Farm ponds for water, fish and livelihoods

the homestead for the home and garden. The excavation becomes the pond. Traditionally, the water collected in the *de facto* pond is used for domestic purposes and to produce aquatic weeds for pigs. Most pig and other manures are used on field crops, especially rice. As fish production grows in importance, more of the manure is diverted to fertilize the pond.

It is estimated that 85 to 90 percent of the rural families maintain a garden and livestock pen, with 30 to 35 percent of these having fishponds. In many villages, 50 to 80 percent of families have the full VAC system. Around 30 to 60 percent of income of most village families may come from the system; in many cases, it may be 100 percent.

Most families keep various animals on the farm, including one or more water buffaloes and cattle, one or more pigs, and several ducks and chickens. The large ruminant animals are allowed to graze or are fed farm by-products. The swine and poultry are usually fed with kitchen wastes, as well as other farm by-products, such as cassava, rice bran, sweet potato, banana trunks and water hyacinth.

A portion of the livestock manure is used to fertilize fruit trees and vegetables. Trees are applied with manure once or twice a year; vegetables are manured according to their needs. Pond silt is removed every 3 to 4 years and used as fertilizer.

The fishpond is usually allocated a more central part of the farm for better management. Pond area ranges from 100 to 1 500 m^2, with a pond depth of about 1 m. Ponds are often drained after the final harvest, usually in February. The bottom of the pond is kept dry for 1 to 3 weeks; after which it is cleaned, limed, manured and then filled up with water for restocking. Domestic washings and kitchen wastes are channeled into the pond daily. Animal manure is also applied twice a month at the rate of 0.05 to 0.15 kg/m^2. Three months after stocking, farmers begin to harvest on a weekly basis using small nets and continuously restock and harvest the pond.

(Source: Le Thanh Luu, in FAO, ICLARM & IIRR 2001)

Annex 2

A checklist for decision and planning

The following checklist list can help organizations decide and develop plans for interventions about choosing small ponds as an option in rural development and livelihood diversification programmes.

1 Do farm ponds already exist in the target community?
2 Do community members like fish?
3 What are the community's priorities and the farmers' motives?
4 Can viable ponds be built in the community?
5 Are water and water-retaining soils present?
6 Which types of farm ponds would best suit a given area?
7 Are there farmers who wish to diversify their activities into farm ponds?
8 Is there sufficient desire and labour among the farmers to build ponds?
9 What are the traditional and agricultural calendars in the community?
10 During which months could farm ponds be built? Is there sufficient time in the 'off season' to build ponds?
11 Where can fish seed be sourced in the area to initially stock ponds?
12 How will the changing seasons affect fish production?
13 How can the farmers be best organized in groups?
14 Are agricultural by- products available in the area to serve as nutrients to the pond?
15 Is there a source of manures and materials for composting in ponds in the area?
16 Are there rules or regulations governing the building of farm ponds, movement of fish seed or the commerce in farm pond products?

17 Is land tenure to the farm pond site(s) secure and documented?

18 Are water rights secure and documented?

19 What is the potential for expansion of farm ponds in the area? Land area, water supply, labour?

20 Are there irrigation schemes in the area where ponds could be built?

21 Are there schools in the area where a farm pond could be built as a practical teaching tool?

22 How can available resources best be used for farm ponds and fish production?

23 Is there a market for fish in the area?

24 Which species of fish is most preferred in the area?

25 Are fish processed in the area? If so, how are they processed and by whom? What is the shelf-life of such fish?

26 Would it be feasible to integrate small livestock and/or crops with ponds? Are there examples of integrated small farms in the area where training could be done?

27 Does the organization have sufficient human and financial resources to support the farm pond programme?

28 Does the organization have the resources to adequately provide this support until it can be taken over by the smallholder organization?

29 Who are the other actors that could benefit from intervention (e.g., government agents, researchers, etc.)?

30 Is there an extension service or other body already supporting the community to develop farm ponds?

Selected further reading

Behera, U. K., Yates, C. M., Kebreab, E. & France, J. 2008. Farming systems methodology for efficient resource management at the farm level: A review from an Indian perspective. *Journal of Agricultural Science* 146:493-505.

Bosma R. H., Udo H. M. J.,Verreth J. A. J.,Visser L. E. & Nam C. Q. 2005. Agriculture diversification in the Mekong Delta: farmers' motives and contributions to livelihoods. *Asian Journal of Agriculture and Development* 2 (1&2):49-66.

Brummett, R. E. 2003. Aquaculture and society in the 21st century. *World Aquaculture* 34(1):51-59.

Brummett, R. E. 2002. Realizing the potential of integrated aquaculture. *In* N. Uphoff (ed). *Agro-ecological Innovations: Increasing Food Production with Participatory Development*. Earthscan, London.

Brummett, R. E. 2000. Factors affecting fish prices in southern Malawi. *Aquaculture* 186 (3,4):243-251.

Brummett, R. E., Jere, D. J. J. & Pouomogne,V. 2004. A farmer-participatory approach to aquaculture technology development & dissemination. *Uganda Journal of Agricultural Sciences* 9(1):530-536.

Brummett, R. E., Lazard, J. & Moehl, J. 2008. African aquaculture: realizing the potential. *Food Policy* 33:371-385.

Brummett, R. E., Gockowski,J., Bakwowi, J. & Etaba, A. D. 2004. Analysis of aquaculture investments in periurban Yaoundé, Cameroon. *Aquaculture Economics & Management* 8(5/6):1-10.

Brummett, R. E. & Costa-Pierce, B. A. 2002. Village-based aquaculture ecosystems as a model for sustainable aquaculture development in sub-Saharan Africa. *In* B.A. Costa-Pierce (Ed.), *Ecological Aquaculture: the Evolution of the Blue Revolution.* Blackwell Science, Oxford, UK.

Brummett, R. E. & Williams, M. J. 2000. Aquaculture in African rural and economic development. *Ecological Economics* 33(2):193-203.

Brummett, R.E. & R. P. Noble. 1995. *Aquaculture for African smallholders.* ICLARM Technical Report 46. World Fish Center, Penang, Malaysia.

Calub, B. M. 2003. *Participatory rural appraisal guidebook.* Farming Systems and Soil Resources Institute, University of the Philippines, Los Baños.

Camagni, R., Gibelli, M. C. & Rigamonti, P. 2002. Urban mobility and urban form: the social and environmental costs of different patterns of urban expansion. *Ecological Economics* 40:199-216.

De Gorter, H. & Tsur, Y. 1991. Explaining price policy bias in agriculture: the calculus of support-maximizing politicians. *American Journal of Agricultural Economics* 73(4):1244-1254.

Dela Cruz, C. R., Lightfoot, C., Costa-Pierce, B. A., Carangal, V. R. & Bimbao, M. P. (eds.) 1992. *Rice-fish research and development in Asia.* ICLARM Conference Prococeedings No. 24, 457 pp.

Delgado, C. L., Hopkins, J. & Kelly,V. A. 1998. *Agricultural growth linkages in sub-Saharan Africa.* Research Report 107. International Food Policy Research Institute, Washington, D.C.

Dey, M. M., Kambewa, P., Prein, M., Jamu, D., Paraguas, F. J., Pemsl, D. & Briones, R. M. 2007. Impact of the development and dissemination of integrated aquaculture-agriculture technologies in Malawi. p. 118-146 *In* H. Waibel & D. Zilberman eds., *International Research on Natural Resource Management: Advances in Impact Assessment.* CABI Publishing, Wallingford, UK.

Dey, M. M., Kambewa P., Prein, M., Jamu, D., Paraguas, F. J., Pemsl, D. E. & Briones, R. M. 2006. Impact of development and dissemination of integrated aquaculture-agriculture (IAA) technologies in Malawi. Naga, *WorldFish Center Quarterly* 29(1&2):28-35.

Edwards, P., Little, D. C. & Demaine, H. (eds.) 2002. Rural aquaculture in Asia. CAB International (AIT and DFID), Wallingford, UK. 358 p.

Edwards, P., Demaine, H., Innes-Taylor, N. & Turongruang, D. 1996. Sustainable aquaculture for small-scale farmers: need for a balanced model. *Outlook on Agriculture* 25(1):19-26.

Erskine, J. M. 1997. Sustainability measures for natural resources. *In* G. Shivakoti, G. Varughese, E. Ostrom, A. Shukla & G. Thapa (eds), *People and Participation in Sustainable Development. Workshop on Political Theory and Policy Analysis*, Indiana University, Bloomington, USA.

FAO. 2006a. *Regional review on aquaculture development 4. Sub-Saharan Africa 2005*, by T. Hecht, Rome.

FAO. 2006b. *Guiding principles for promoting aquaculture in Africa: benchmarks for sustainable development,* by J.Moehl, R.E. Brummett, B.M. Kalende & A. Coche. CIFA Occasional Paper 28, Accra.

FAO. 2005. *Report of the FAO-World Fish Center workshop on small-scale aquaculture in sub-Saharan Africa: revisiting the aquaculture target group paradigm,* by J. Moehl, M. Halwart & R.E. Brummett, CIFA Occasional Paper 25, Rome.

FAO. 2004. *Aquaculture extension in sub-Saharan Africa, ,* by R.E. Brummett, V. Pouomogne & A.G. Coche. FAO Fisheries Circular No. 1002, Rome.

FAO. 2003a. *Culture of fish in rice fields*, M. Halwart & M.V. Gupta (eds), FAO, Rome and WorldFish Center, Penang.

FAO. 2003b. *Integrated livestock-fish farming systems*, by D.C.Little & P.Edwards, Rome.

FAO. 2001b. The VAC System in Northern Vietnam, by Le Than Luu, *In Integrated Agriculture-Aquacuture Systems: A primer*. FAO Fisheries Technical Paper 407. FAO, ICLARM, IIRR.

FAO. 2000. *Small ponds make a big difference*, Rome.

FAO. 1997. *Report of the expert consultation on small-scale rural aquaculture*. Fisheries Report 548, Rome.

FAO. 1994. *Handbook on small-scale freshwater fish farming*, Rome.

FAO. 1992. *Fish culture in undrainable ponds, a manual of extension* Fisheries Technical Paper 325, Rome.

FAO. 1990. *Better Freshwater Fish Farming: Raising Fish in Pens and Cages*, Better Farming Series 38, Rome.

FAO. 1986. *Better Freshwater Fish Farming: Further Improvement,* Better Farming Series 35, Rome.

FAO. 1982. *Aquaculture Extension Services Review*. FAO Fisheries Cirircular No. 747, by M.S. Chakroff, Rome.

FAO. 1981a. *Better Freshwater Fish Farming: the Fish*, Better Farming Series 30, Rome.

FAO. 1981b. *Freshwater Fish Farming: the Pond*, Better Farming Series 29, Rome.

FAO. 1981c. *Water: Where Water Comes From*, Better Farming Series 28, FAO, Rome.

FAO. 1975. *La Rizipisciculture et les Elevages Associes en Afrique*, by M. M. J. Vincke, FAO, Rome.

FAO, ICLARM & IIRR. 2001. *Integrated agriculture-aquaculture: a primer*, FAO Fisheries Technical Paper 407, Rome.

Gomez, A.A. 1994. Research-extension linkage: an important component of technology transfer and adoption. *Journal of the Asian Farming Systems Association* 2(2):197-204.

Gupta, M.V., Mazid, M.A., Islam, M.S., Rahman, M., Hussain, M.G. 1999. *Integration of Aquaculture into the Farming Systems of the Floodprone Ecosystems of Bangladesh: an Evaluation of Adoption and Impact*. ICLARM Technical Reports No. 56. International Center for Living Aquatic Resources Management, Manila.

Gupta, M.V. Sollows, J.D., Mazid, M.A., Rahman, M., Hussain, M.G. & Dey, M.M. 1998. *Integrating Aquaculture With Rice Farming in Bangladesh: Feasibility and Economic Viability, its Adoption and Impact*. ICLARM Technical Reports No. 55, International Center for Living Aquatic Resources Management, Manila.

Halwart, M., Moehl, J., Prein, M. & Jia, J. 2008. SPADA – the Special Programme for Aquaculture Development in Africa. Selected Highlight. *FAO Aquaculture Newsletter* 40: 33–35.

Halwart, M. & Overton,J.L. 2001. Introducing aquaculture into farming systems: what to look out for. p. 48-51. *In* IIRR, IDRC, FAO, NACA & ICLARM. (eds.) *Utilizing Different Aquatic Resources for Livelihoods in Asia: a Resource Book*. International Institute of Rural Reconstruction, Silang, Cavite, Philippines.

Harrison, E. 1994. Aquaculture in Africa: socio-economic dimensions, p. 240-299 *In* J.F. Muir & R. J. Roberts, eds., *Recent Advances in Aquaculture*, Blackwell Science, Oxford, UK.

Harrison, E., Stewart, J.A. Stirrat,R.L. & Muir,J. 1994. *Fish Farming in Africa – What's the Catch?* Overseas Development Administration & University of Sussex, UK.

Hopkins, K. D. & Cruz, E. M. 1982. *The ICLARM-CLSU Integrated Animal-fish farming project: Final Report*. ICLARM Technical Report No 5. International Center for Living Aquatic Resources Management, Manila.

ICLARM. 1982. *Integrated Farming: China, Java, Mexico, Philippines, Thailand*. ICLARM Newsletter. Vol.5, No.3.

IIRR, IDRC, FAO, NACA & ICLARM. (eds.) 2001. *Utilizing different aquatic resources for livelihoods in ASIA, a resource book*. International Institute of Rural Reconstruction, Silang, Cavite, Philippines. 416 p.

Karim, M., Ahmed, M., Talukder, R. K., Taslim, M. A. & Rahman, H. Z. 2006. *Dynamic agri-business-focused aquaculture for poverty reduction and economic growth in Bangladesh*. World Fish Center Discussion Series 1, WorldFish Cener, Penang, Malaysia.

Kuyvenhoven, A. & Ruben, R. 2002. Economic conditions for sustainable agricultural intensification, pp. 58-70, *In* N. Uphoff, Ed, *Agro-Ecological Innovations; Increasing Food Production with Participatory Development*, Earthscan Publications, Ltd, London.

Lazard, J., Lecomte,Y., Tomal, B. & Weigel,J. Y. 1991. *Pisciculture en Afrique SubSaharienne*. Ministère de la Coopération et du Développement, Paris.

Lightfoot, C. & Noble, R. P. 1993. A participatory experiment in sustainable agriculture. *Journal for Farming Systems Research & Extension* 4(1):11-34.

Lightfoot, C. M., Prein, M., Ofori, J. K. 1996. Analytical framework for rethinking aquaculture development for smallholder farmers. p. 4-10 In: Prein, M., Ofori, J.K. and Lightfoot, C. (eds.) *Research for the future development of aquaculture in Ghana*. ICLARM Conference Proceedings 42, 94 p.

Lightfoot, C., Bimbao, M. P. & Dalsgaard,P. T. & Pullin, R. S. V. 1993. Aquaculture and sustainability through integrated resource management. *Outlook in Agriculture* 22(3):143-150.

Lightfoot, C., Dalsgaard, P., Bimbao, M. P. & Fermin, F. 1993. Farming participatory procedures for managing and monitoring sustainable farming systems. *Journal of the Asian Farming systems Association* 2(2):67-87.

Lovshin, L. L., Schwartz, N. B. & Hatch, U. 2000. Impacts of integrated fish culture on resource limited farms in Guatemala and Panamá. *Research and Development Series* 46, International Center of Aquaculture and Aquatic Environments, Auburn, Alabama, USA.

Lustig, N., Arias, O. & Rigolini, J. 2002. *Poverty reduction and economic growth; a two-way causality.* Sustainable Development Department Technical Paper POV-111, Inter-American Development Bank, Washington, DC.

Mathias, J. A., Charles, A. T., Baotong, H. 2001. *Integrated Fish Farming,* CRC Press, New York, USA.

Miller, J. W., Stafford, J. & des Poissons, S. E. 1978. *Guide de Vulgarisation Piscicole en Afrique.* FAO Projet de Vulgarisation Piscicole, OTC Project de Développement Communautaire, Corps de la Paix. Imprimerie Saint-Paul, Bangui, RCA.

Ministry of Livestock, Fisheries and Animal Industries-Cameroon, FAO, Development Agricultural Research Institute & WorldFish Center. 2003. *Strategic Framework for Sustainable Aquaculture Development in Cameroon.*

Mosse, D., Farrington, J. & Rew, A. 1998. *Development as Process; Concepts and Methods for Working with Complexity.* Development Policy Series, Routledge, London.

Nerlove, M., Vosti, S. & Basel, W. 1996. *Role of farm-level diversification in the adoption of modern technology in Brazil*. Research Report 104. International Food Policy Research Institute, Washington, D.C.

Nhan, D. K., Phong, L. T., Verdegem, M. J. C., Duong, L. T., Bosma, R. H. & Little, D. C. 2007. Integrated freshwater aquaculture, crop and livestock production in the Mekong delta, Vietnam: determinants and the role of the pond. *Agricultural Systems* 94(2):445-458.

Pant J., Demaine H. & Edwards P. 2005. Bio-resource flow in integrated agriculture-aquaculture systems in a tropical monsoonal climate: A case study in Northeast Thailand. *Agricultural Systems.* 83(2):203-219.

Potengham, K., & Miller, J. 2006. *Catfish Hatchery and Production Manual*. Food Security Programme Publication, NSPFS/FAO, Rome.

Prein, M. 2002. Integration of aquaculture into crop-animal systems in Asia. *Agricultural Systems* 71:127-146.

Prein, M., Oficial, R. T., Bimbao, M. A. & Lopez, T. S. 2002. Aquaculture for diversification of small farms within forest buffer zone management: an example from the uplands of Quirino Province, Philippines. p. 97-109. *In* P. Edwards, D.C. Little & H. Demaine (eds.) *Rural aquaculture in Asia.* CAB International (AIT and DFID), Wallingford, UK.

Pullin, R. S. V. 1998. Aquaculture, integrated resources management and the environment. p. 19-43. *In* J.A. Mathias, A.T. Charles & H. Baotong (eds.) *Integrated Fish Farming,* CRC Press, Boca Raton.

Pullin, R. S. V. & Prein, M. 1995. Fishponds facilitate natural resources management on small-scale farms in tropical developing countries. p. 169-186 *In* J.-J. Symoens and J.-C. Micha (eds.) *The management of integrated freshwater agro-piscicultural ecosystems in tropical areas.* 587 p. Technical Centre for Agricultural and Rural Co-operation (CTA), Wageningen, and Belgian Royal Academy of Overseas Sciences (ARSOM), Brussels.

Reij, C. & Waters-Bayer, A. (eds). 2001. *Farmer innovation in Africa: a Source of Inspiration*. Earthscan Publications, London.

Roos, N, Islam, M. & Thilsted, S.H. 2003. Small indigenous fish species in aquaculture in Bangladesh: contribution to vitamin A, calcium and iron intakes. *Journal of Nutrition* 133:4021S-6S.

Ruddle, K. and Prein, M. 1998. Assessing the potential nutritional and household economic benefits of developing integrated farming systems. p. 111-121 *In* J.A. Mathias, A.T. Charles and H. Baotong (eds.) *Integrated Fish Farming*, CRC Press, Boca Raton. 420 p.

Sanders, J.H., Shapiro,B. I & Ramaswamy, S. 1996. *The economics of agricultural technology in semiarid sub-Saharan Africa*. Johns Hopkins University Press, Baltimore, Maryland, USA.

Shivakoti, G., Varughese, G., Ostrom, E., Shukla, A. & Thapa, G. (eds). 1997. *People and participation in sustainable development*. Workshop on Political Theory and Policy Analysis, Indiana University, Bloomington, USA.

Stark, D. 1989. Review: entrepreneurs on the road to post-communism. *Contemporary Sociology* 18(5):671-674.

Szelenyi, I. 1988. *Socialist Entrepreneurs: Embourgeoisement in Rural Hungary*. University of Wisconsin Press, Madison, USA.

Tambi, N. E. 2001. Analysis of household attitudes toward the purchase of livestock products and fish in Cameroon. *Agricultural Economics* 26(2):135-147.

UNDP, NORAD, & FAO. 1987. *Thematic Evaluation of Aquaculture. A joint study*. United Nations Development Programme, New York, Norwegian Ministry of Development Cooperation, Oslo, and FAO, Rome.

Farm ponds for water, fish and livelihoods

Uphoff, N. (ed). 2002. *Agro-ecological innovations; increasing food production with participatory development.* Earthscan Publications, Ltd., London.

Van Der Zijpp, A. J., Verreth, J. A. J., Tri, L. Q., van Mensvoort, M. E. F., Bosma, R.H. & Beveridge, M.C.M. (eds.) 2007. *Fishponds in farming systems.* Wageningen, Wageningen Academic Publishers

Winkelmann, D. L. 1998. *CGIAR Activities and goals: tracing the connections. Issues in Agriculture.* The Consultative Group for International Agricultural Research, World Bank, Washington, D.C.

World Bank. 2006. *Aquaculture: Changing the Face of the Waters. Meeting the Promise and Challenge of Sustainable Aquaculture.* Agriculture and Rural Development. Rept.# 36622-GLB.

Yong Sulem, S. & Brummett, R. E. 2006. Intensity and profitability of *Clarias gariepinus* nursing systems in Yaoundé, Cameroon. *Aquaculture Research* 37:601-605.

Sources of further information and support

Aquaculture Network of Africa (ANAF)
http://www.anafaquaculture.net

Aquaculture Association of Southern Africa (AASA)
http://www.aasa-aqua.co.za/

Aquaculture Network Information Center
http://aquanic.org/

FAO – Fisheries and Aquaculture Division
http://www.fao.org/fishery/aquaculture/en

International Livestock Research Institute
http://www.ilri.org/

International Institute of Tropical Agriculture
http://www.iita.org/

International Water Management Institute
http://www.iwmi.cgiar.org/

International Rice Research Institute
http://www.irri.org/

Network of Aquaculture Centers in Asia
http://www.enaca.org

Sustainable Aquaculture Research Networks in sub-Saharan Africa
http://www.sarnissa.org

World Aquaculture Society
https://www.was.org/Main/Default.asp

WorldFish Center
http://www.worldfishcenter.org/v2/index.html

Notes

Notes